Contents

Written by Lisa Regan
Illustrated by Angelika Scudamore

First published 2015 by Brown Watson
The Old Mill, 76 Fleckney Road
Kibworth Beauchamp
Leicestershire LE8 0HG

ISBN: 978 0 7097 2295 3
© 2015 Brown Watson, England
Reprinted 2016, 2018 (twice)
Printed in Malaysia

Now I Can

READ

Adventure Stories

Brown Watson

ENGLAND

Prince Louie and his Horse

Once upon a time, there was a knight called Louie. He rode on a majestic brown horse, with a flowing mane and a fine tail.

Louie's father, the king, had to go to battle against an evil king. All of their soldiers lined up on the battlefield. Louie heard the blast of a trumpet, and all the soldiers went thundering off on their horses.

Louie's horse was called Neptune, and it was afraid of all the noise on the battlefield. It turned around and galloped off, carrying Louie with it. They ran and ran until they reached the sea.

When they got to the water's edge, Neptune didn't stop running. He carried on into the waves until they reached his head. Louie begged for him to stop.

As they got deeper and deeper into the ocean, Louie realised that he could still breathe underwater. He looked down and, to his surprise, Neptune had changed. He had become a seahorse!

Together, they swam through the ocean depths until they reached a palace. It was the home of the Sea King. He told Louie to stay with him until all the wars on land were over. It was the safest place to be, and such fun!

Read these words again

noise	running
battle	knight
waves	trumpet
flowing	surprise
together	soldier
breathe	majestic
another	galloped

What can you see here?

crab

Sea King

seahorse

fish

starfish

horse

From Rags to Riches

Josie was a good,
hard working girl, who helped
her poorly mother with all the
household chores. Her mother
loved her very much, and was
very grateful. But they
were very poor.

One day, Josie's sister brought
home a dirty old rug. 'Please
will you wash it, so I can put it
in my room?' she begged. Josie
sighed, but promised to help.

That night, after Josie had cooked and washed up and put all of her brothers and sisters to bed, she sat down with the rug on her knee. It was full of holes, and needed mending.

As Josie sewed up the holes, she felt the rug wriggle in her hands. Peculiar! She put down her needle and thread, and laid the rug on the floor. It began to float and fly!

Nervously, Josie stepped onto the rug and sat down. It lifted higher into the air, and then flew straight out of the window! Together, they soared over the land, and settled by some trees.

To Josie's amazement, the trees were loaded with golden coins. She picked a few and put them in her pockets. The rug carried her back home, and her family all hugged her when they realised they were now rich!

Read these words again

mother   promised

float   stepped

higher   realised

clean   pockets

cooked   peculiar

window   straight

sewed   nervously

What can you see here?

bowls

train

rug

cotton reel

gold coins

tree

Sailing the Seas

Harry loved to read. His favourite books were about pirates, and shipwrecks, and sea monsters. One night, as he turned out his light and put his book away, he heard a strange splashing noise.

Harry lay in the darkness and was sure he felt moisture on his face. He could taste salt and hear the crashing of waves and the creaking of wooden boards. Then he heard a voice.
'Ahoy there!'

The voice belonged to a
pirate! 'Come with me, lad,'
said the pirate. 'And bring your
sword!' Harry jumped up and
clasped the pirate's hand. With
a whoosh and a flash, he found
himself on a boat.

The deck was swarming with
pirates, who handed Harry some
clothes and a sword. 'Prepare
for battle!' they cried, and ran
to the cannon at the front of
the boat.

'Take aim and FIRE!' shouted a voice, and Harry wondered what they were firing at. He couldn't see any other ships. Then he saw a giant tentacle creeping over the edge of the boat.

Harry lunged with his sword. He danced and jabbed until the sea monster splashed into the ocean, defeated. The pirates all cheered. Then he fell back into bed, exhausted. What an adventure!

Read these words again

edge

light

battle

noise

danced

cannon

flash

jumped

cheered

darkness

ocean

sword

monsters

exhausted

What can you see here?

cannonballs

moon

rat

window

pirate

book

Being Brave

Once upon a time, an evil monster roamed the country, catching children to keep in his magic tower. It had no doors and no stairs, and only one small window at the very top.

The tower had a single room, high above the ground, where all the children lived together. They were very frightened of the monster, and cried whenever he appeared.

The room was dusty and smelly, and full of spiders. They peered at the children from the darkness, and the children huddled together as far from them as possible.

One day, the monster brought a small boy to the tower. He was tiny and scared, and the other children looked after him. Soon he grew less nervous, and began to explore.

The little boy walked to the corner of the room where the spiders lived. The other children shrieked and trembled. But this boy wasn't afraid of spiders, and soon became their friend.

Before long, the spiders had spun a beautiful rope made of silk. It reached all the way from the window to the ground, so the children could climb down and run away. The monster never saw any of them again!

Read these words again

dusty

single

children

explore

spiders

climb

country

monster

appeared

darkness

shrieked

friend

whenever

frightened

What can you see here?

rabbit

rainbow

spider

butterfly

lamp

lizard

New Friends

It was an ordinary day, and Flash was having fun with his friends. They loved to rev their engines, and blink their lights on and off at each other. Then they would hurtle off around the yard, tooting their horns and having a race.

Flash loved his friends. They always looked out for each other, and hardly ever crashed. They were like one big, happy family.

The little cars stopped racing to watch a huge truck pull into the yard. It growled to a halt, and looked around. 'Which one of you is Flash?' it asked.

Flash nervously crept forward. 'Come with me!' said the truck, and lowered its ramps. The cars all watched as Flash carefully drove up onto the back of the truck. Then they tooted and flashed as it drove out onto the open road.

The truck took Flash to a large, dusty area surrounded by high fences. Flash was scared. He wanted to be back with his friends.

Then a bright red racing car roared up. 'Welcome to the track!' it thundered. Flash was going to be a racing car! Soon, he had lots of new friends, and they all looked after each other, too. Flash felt very lucky indeed.

Read these words again

racing   lights
looked   engines
around   carefully
asked   welcome
hardly   roared
forward   ordinary
family   surrounded

What can you see here?

bird

car

flag

tyre

petrol
drums

bunting

On the Lookout

Joe loved to climb trees.
He wasn't afraid of anything,
even when his mummy told him
it might be dangerous. He
scrambled up to the top of the
highest branches and swayed
in the breeze.

'I can see for miles!' he called.
Sure enough, Joe could look out
across the valley and see a castle
and a winding river. There were
fields full of farm animals that
looked like tiny dots.

Michael also loved climbing. He was just as brave as Joe, and would race him to the top of the next tree. His mummy begged him to hold on tight, and come down at once.

'But I can see everything!' he laughed. From the treetops he could see as far as the coast. There was a lighthouse, and boats, and a little train chugging towards the seaside town.

Jonty didn't like to climb. He preferred to keep his feet firmly on the ground to do his exploring. But he still saw amazing things. He just had to look more carefully.

'It's like a jungle!' he told them, as he lay on the grass. 'There are wild animals, and giant plants, and exotic creatures. AND I won't fall off the floor!' he laughed.

Read these words again

climb	everything
ground	exploring
branches	amazing
tight	laughed
seaside	exotic
coast	windmill
highest	dangerous

What can you see here?

windmill

train

ladybird

lighthouse

yacht

bee

Sir Chancelot to the Rescue

Sir Chancelot was bored. There were no damsels to rescue, so he sat in his kitchen to have a bite to eat. But something strange was happening on his plate. His egg was shaking, and making a noise!

He gently tapped the shell, and was surprised when a tiny face appeared through the crack. This was no ordinary egg. It was a dragon egg! Sir Chancelot carefully helped the tiny creature to free itself.

Now Sir Chancelot had a problem. Knights don't like dragons. They fight them! But this one cuddled up to him and squeaked gently when he stroked it. The two of them became best friends.

As the dragon grew larger and larger, it began to take over the whole house. Its wings filled the great hall, and its fiery breath shot up the chimney and scorched the curtains.
What was to be done?

There was no way around it. The dragon had to move out! So Sir Chancelot built a home for it on the edge of the forest. The dragon flew to the castle every day to see him, and helped to keep his enemies away.

Soon, everyone in the land had heard of the dragon. Every day, there was a new damsel to rescue. They all wanted to meet the famous Sir Chancelot and his unusual pet!

Read these words again

shell   breath

castle   edge

rescue   famous

around   problem

whole   appeared

curtains   enemies

chimney   fiery

What can you see here?

cloud

dragon

wooden spoons

plate

dragon
egg

pots

Land Ahoy!

Pedro was no ordinary boy. His father was a pirate, so Pedro spent his life on a ship. It was a very hard life. The pirates were smelly and rude, and treated Pedro like a slave.

Pedro worked all day long. He had to scrub the decks, wash the clothes, peel the vegetables, milk the cow, sweep the floors, and then scrub the decks all over again.

It didn't matter how fast Pedro cleaned, for the pirates made mess even faster. They made fun of him, too. 'Aharrrr, young Pedro!' they bawled. 'You'll never be a pirate. You're too small and skinny to fight!'

Times were hard, and the supplies on board were running low. They needed to stock up on food and water. But no one knew where the nearest land was.

None of the pirates could see
anything through their telescope.
They were all too old or fat to
climb up into the crow's nest.
Pedro saw his chance to
be helpful.

He grabbed the telescope and
scampered up the rigging. Sure
enough, he could see the answer
to their problems. 'Land ahoy!'
he shouted, and all the pirates
did a little jig. Pedro was a hero!

Read these words again

sweep

faster

clothes

treated

worked

fight

helpful

supplies

board

vegetables

nearest

ordinary

anything

through

What can you see here?

palm tree

seagull

cat

wiggly
worm

carrot

bucket

A Very Long Journey

Casey was a very clever boy. He could build anything. Today, he was working on a time machine. 'Time for tea!' shouted his mummy, and Casey put down his tools.

After tea, Casey loaded up the cargo hold with toys, drinks and snacks. He kissed his mummy goodbye and closed the door. 'Make sure you're back for bedtime!' she shouted, and waved him off.

The time machine rattled and buzzed and juddered. Then it landed with a bump, and Casey jumped out to explore. He took his sword and shield with him, just in case.

Casey crept through the trees. He could hear rustling, and see footprints in the mud. How far had he travelled? Where had he landed? He hoped he wasn't in the jungle with tigers watching him!

As Casey peered through the bushes, he saw a tail. Then he heard a roar coming from high above him. Maybe he was about to come face to face with a dragon? Casey looked up and gasped.

He had travelled further than he thought – all the way back in time to when dinosaurs were alive. He tiptoed backwards and jumped into his time machine. Suddenly, bed seemed like a very safe place to be!

Read these words again

jungle	further
dragon	gasped
shouted	machine
kissed	footprints
snacks	rustling
closed	journey
landed	loaded

What can you see here?

toolbox

screwdriver

nails

hammer

time machine

footprints

Ocean Rescue

Leo and his parents were taking a trip. They were on a boat, surrounded by beautiful blue ocean. Leo had caught some fish that they were going to eat for supper.

Suddenly, a great storm blew up. The waves lashed over the side of their little boat, and threw it high in the air. The boat tipped over, and another enormous wave smashed it into little pieces.

Leo clung to a piece of wood
to stay afloat. He was very
frightened. Gradually, the storm
died down and the waves grew
small again. But Leo's parents
were nowhere to be seen.

Leo bobbed in the water,
wondering what to do. He was
trying to be brave, but he
wanted to go home. Then
something swam up beside him.
He hoped it wasn't a
hungry shark!

Luckily for Leo, it was a friendly whale. It snorted gently, and a fountain of water lifted Leo high into the air. He landed – PLOP! – right on the whale's back.

The whale swam smoothly towards the shore. 'Look!' shouted Leo. 'Mummy! Daddy!' His parents were clinging to each other in the blue ocean. The whale scooped them up as well, and carried them all back to shore.

Read these words again

supper   afloat

ocean   nowhere

whale   towards

hungry   fountain

suddenly   enormous

beside   frightened

pieces   wondering

What can you see here?

octopus

tree

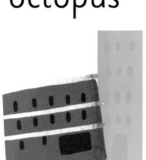

buildings

purple fish

crab

lightning

An Alien Adventure

Harry and Hannah were having problems. BIG problems. With a crash and a clunk, their rocket hit the surface of a planet. This was not where they were supposed to land!

Harry cautiously opened the door, and Hannah jumped out. The planet was nothing like Earth. It was covered in fine, powdery dust that was a strange gold colour.

The two astronauts held hands, so they didn't lose each other, and began to explore. As they walked around the edge of a giant boulder, Hannah pulled on Harry's hand and tugged him back to hide.

Harry and Hannah watched a crowd of strange creatures come towards them. They were pushing each other and shouting in a strange language. They didn't seem very friendly at all.

Then the aliens caught sight of the two astronauts. They stopped and pointed, and then began to move closer and closer. Help!

When they were within touching distance, one alien lifted up his arms to stop the others. He held up a football and spoke to the astronauts. Yes, of course they wanted to play! Football on another planet is always great fun!

Read these words again

spoke   language
giant   creatures
rocket   distance
stopped   astronauts
covered   boulder
walked   pointed
problems   caught

What can you see here?

green alien

space boot

planet

shooting star

astronaut

rocket